Count **10** across on each line
and colour the numbers.

1	2	3	4	5	6	7	8	9	10
11	12	13	14	15	16	17	18	19	20
21	22	23	24	25	26	27	28	29	30
31	32	33	34	35	36	37	38	39	40
41	42	43	44	45	46	47	48	49	50
51	52	53	54	55	56	57	58	59	60
61	62	63	64	65	66	67	68	69	70
71	72	73	74	75	76	77	78	79	80
81	82	83	84	85	86	87	88	89	90
91	92	93	94	95	96	97	98	99	100

Write the **10** family.

Count in **10**s and fill in
the missing numbers.

3

Draw **10** hairs on each caterpillar.
Write the number of hairs under each caterpillar.

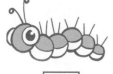

$\boxed{10}$ = $\boxed{10}$ hairs

$\boxed{}$ + $\boxed{}$ = $\boxed{20}$ hairs

$\boxed{}$ + $\boxed{}$ + $\boxed{}$ = $\boxed{}$ hairs

$\boxed{}$ + $\boxed{}$ + $\boxed{}$ + $\boxed{}$ = $\boxed{}$ hairs

$\boxed{}$ + $\boxed{}$ + $\boxed{}$ + $\boxed{}$ + $\boxed{}$ = $\boxed{}$ hairs

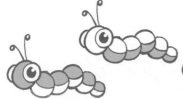

$\boxed{}$ + $\boxed{}$ + $\boxed{}$ + $\boxed{}$ + $\boxed{}$ + $\boxed{}$ = $\boxed{}$ hairs

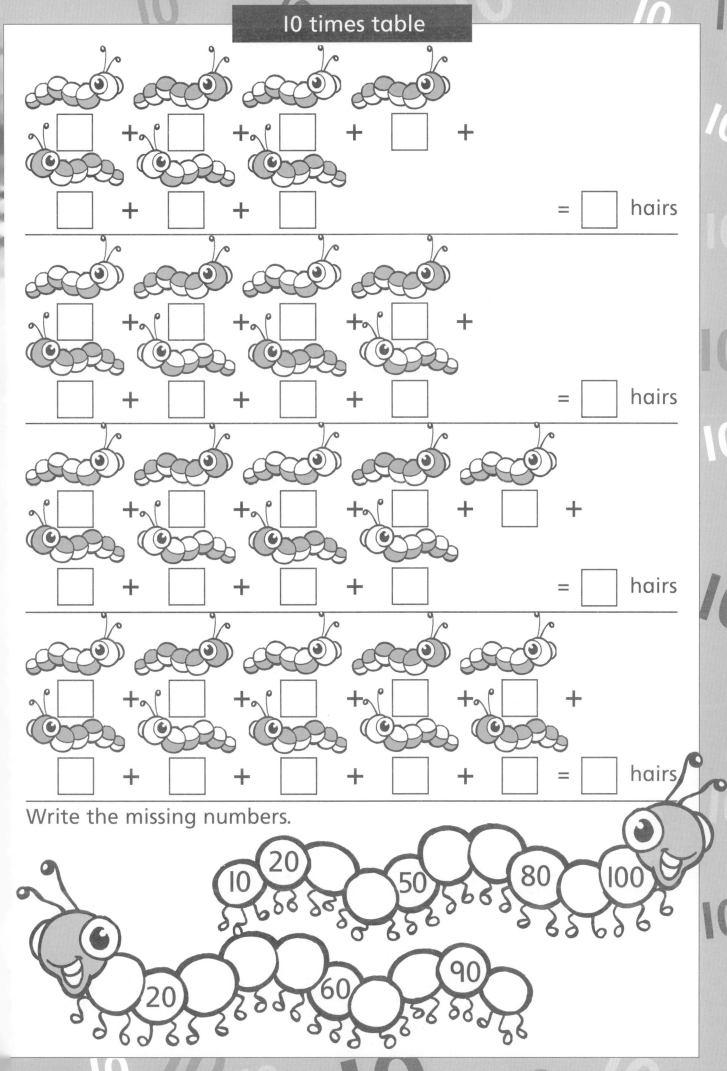

Write the missing numbers.

Put **10** spots on each toadstool.

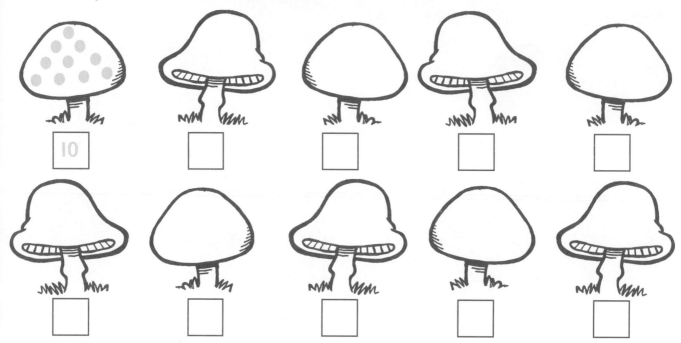

1 toadstool has `10` spots.

2 toadstools have ☐ spots.

3 toadstools have ☐ spots.

4 toadstools have ☐ spots.

5 toadstools have ☐ spots.

6 toadstools have ☐ spots.

7 toadstools have ☐ spots.

8 toadstools have ☐ spots.

9 toadstools have ☐ spots.

10 toadstools have ☐ spots.

1 lot of **10** = `10`   2 lots of **10** = ☐

6 lots of **10** = ☐   9 lots of **10** = ☐

4 lots of **10** = ☐   7 lots of **10** = ☐

How much money?
Write the answers in the boxes.

1 x **10**p = `10 p`

2 x **10**p = `p`

3 x **10**p = `p`

4 x **10**p = `p`

5 x **10**p = `p`

6 x **10**p = `p`

7 x **10**p = `p`

8 x **10**p = `p`

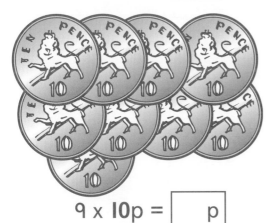

9 x **10**p = `p`

10 x **10**p = `p`

Count the petals on each flower and write the number in the box.

10	10								

Multiply by 10.

2 x 10 = ◯

1 x 10 = ⬡

2 x 10 = ⬡

3 x 10 = ⬡

4 x 10 = ⬡

7 x 10 = ◯

9 x 10 = ◯

5 x 10 = ⬡

6 x 10 = ⬡

7 x 10 = ⬡

4 x 10 = ◯

8 x 10 = ⬡

9 x 10 = ⬡

10 x 10 = ◯

10 x 10 = ⬡

5 x 10 = ◯

Find the multiples of 10.

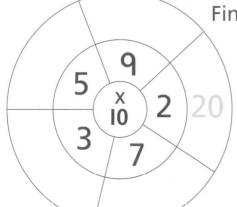

8 x 10 = ◯

10 x 10 = ◯

7 x 10 = ◯

5 x 10 = ◯

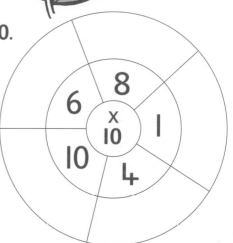

Count **5** across on each line and colour the numbers.

Write the **5** family.

1	2	3	4	5
6	7	8	9	10
11	12	13	14	15
16	17	18	19	20
21	22	23	24	25
26	27	28	29	30
31	32	33	34	35
36	37	38	39	40
41	42	43	44	45
46	47	48	49	50

5

45

25

10

5

Count in **5**s and fill in the missing numbers.

9

Draw **5** spots on each ladybird.
Write the number of spots under each ladybird.

[5] = [5] spots

[5] + [5] = [ ] spots

[ ] + [ ] + [ ] = [ ] spots

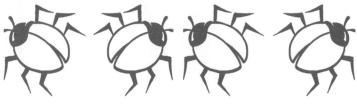

[ ] + [ ] + [ ] + [ ] = [ ] spots

[ ] + [ ] + [ ] + [ ] + [ ] = [ ] spots

[ ] + [ ] + [ ] + [ ] + [ ] + [ ] = [ ] spots

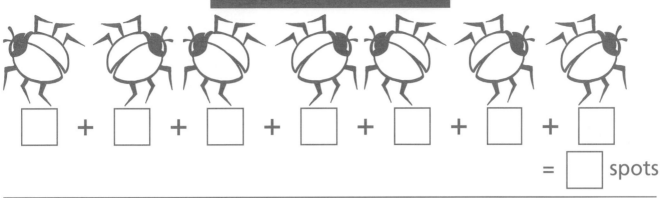

□ + □ + □ + □ + □ + □ + □

= □ spots

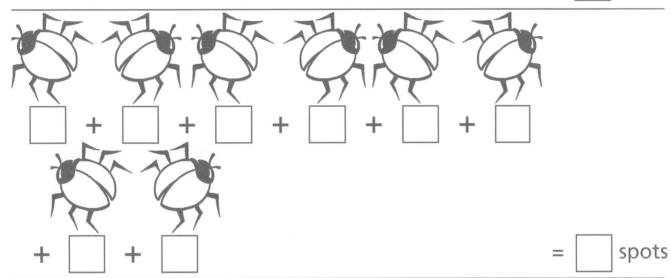

□ + □ + □ + □ + □ + □

+ □ + □ = □ spots

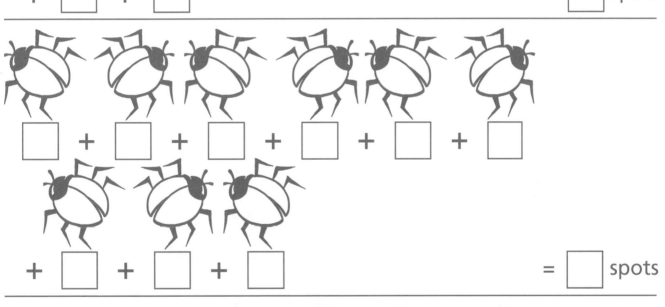

□ + □ + □ + □ + □ + □

+ □ + □ + □ = □ spots

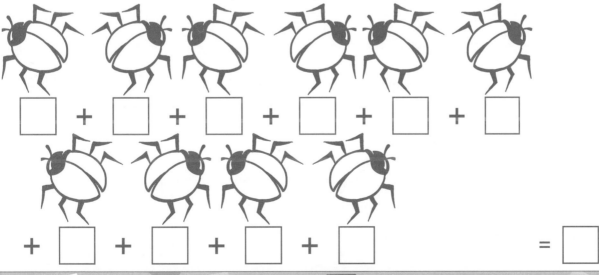

□ + □ + □ + □ + □ + □

+ □ + □ + □ + □ = □ spots

Draw **5** eyes on each alien.

1 alien has [5] eyes.

2 aliens have [ ] eyes.

3 aliens have [ ] eyes.

4 aliens have [ ] eyes.

5 aliens have [ ] eyes.

6 aliens have [ ] eyes.

7 aliens have [ ] eyes.

8 aliens have [ ] eyes.

9 aliens have [ ] eyes.

10 aliens have [ ] eyes.

1 lot of **5** = [5]	3 lots of **5** = [ ]	2 lots of **5** = [ ]
8 lots of **5** = [ ]	10 lots of **5** = [ ]	4 lots of **5** = [ ]
6 lots of **5** = [ ]	9 lots of **5** = [ ]	5 lots of **5** = [ ]

How much money?
Write the answers in the boxes.

1 x **5**p = | 5 p |

2 x **5**p = | p |

3 x **5**p = | p |

4 x **5**p = | p |

5 x **5**p = | p |

6 x **5**p = | p |

7 x **5**p = | p |

8 x **5**p = | p |

9 x **5**p = | p |

10 x **5**p = | p |

Count the bobbles on each hat and write the number in the box.

5

$1 \times 5 =$ ⟨5⟩

$2 \times 5 =$ ⟨ ⟩

$3 \times 5 =$ ⟨ ⟩

$4 \times 5 =$ ⟨ ⟩

$5 \times 5 =$ ⟨ ⟩

$6 \times 5 =$ ⟨ ⟩

$7 \times 5 =$ ⟨ ⟩

$8 \times 5 =$ ⟨ ⟩

$9 \times 5 =$ ⟨ ⟩

$10 \times 5 =$ ⟨ ⟩

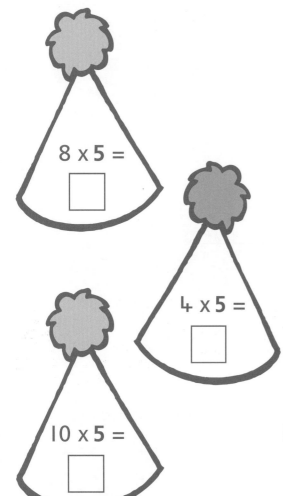

$8 \times 5 =$

$4 \times 5 =$

$10 \times 5 =$

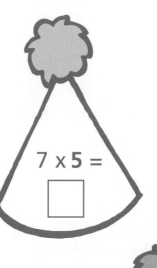

$7 \times 5 =$

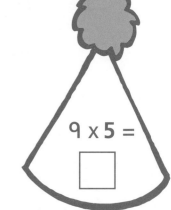

$9 \times 5 =$

Find the multiples of 5.

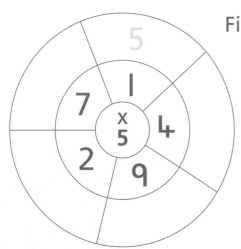

$10 \times 5 =$ ⟨ ⟩

$7 \times 5 =$ ⟨ ⟩

$2 \times 5 =$ ⟨ ⟩

$9 \times 5 =$ ⟨ ⟩

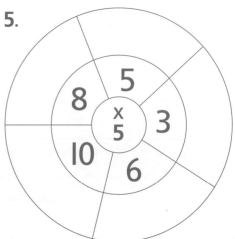

Count **2** across on each line and colour the numbers.

1	2	3	4	5	6	7	8	9	10
11	12	13	14	15	16	17	18	19	20

Colour the **2** family.

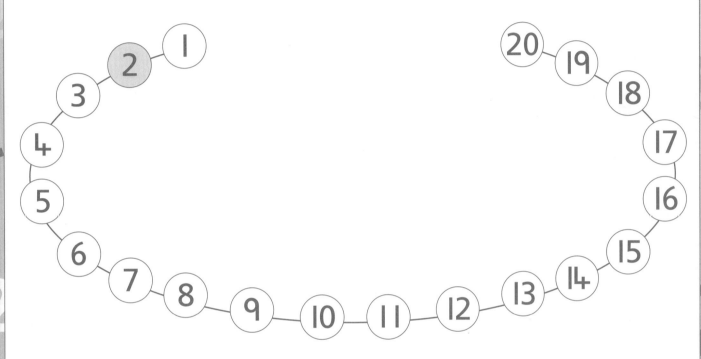

Write the **2** family.

Count in **2**s and fill in the missing numbers.

Draw **2** ears on each teddy.
Write the number of ears under each teddy.

 $=$ 2 ears

 $+$ $=$ ☐ ears

☐ $+$ ☐ $+$ ☐ $=$ ☐ ears

☐ $+$ ☐ $+$ ☐ $+$ ☐ $=$ ☐ ears

☐ $+$ ☐ $+$ ☐ $+$ ☐ $+$ ☐ $=$ ☐ ears

☐ $+$ ☐ $+$ ☐ $+$ ☐ $+$ ☐ $+$ ☐ $=$ ☐ ears

☐ + ☐ + ☐ + ☐ + ☐ + ☐ + ☐

= ☐ ears

☐ + ☐ + ☐ + ☐ + ☐ + ☐

+ ☐ + ☐ = ☐ ears

☐ + ☐ + ☐ + ☐ + ☐ + ☐

+ ☐ + ☐ + ☐ = ☐ ears

☐ + ☐ + ☐ + ☐ + ☐ + ☐

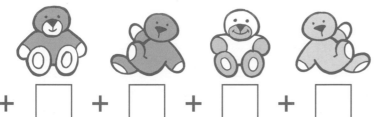

+ ☐ + ☐ + ☐ + ☐ = ☐ ears

Draw **2** scoops of icecream in each cone.

 `2`   ☐   ☐   ☐    ☐

 ☐    ☐   ☐    ☐   ☐

1 cone has `2` scoops.

2 cones have ☐ scoops.

3 cones have ☐ scoops.

4 cones have ☐ scoops.

5 cones have ☐ scoops.

6 cones have ☐ scoops.

7 cones have ☐ scoops.

8 cones have ☐ scoops.

9 cones have ☐ scoops.

10 cones have ☐ scoops.

1 lot of **2** = ☐   10 lots of **2** = ☐   8 lots of **2** = ☐

7 lots of **2** = ☐   5 lots of **2** = ☐   9 lots of **2** = ☐

How much money?
Write the answers in the boxes.

1 x **2p** = [2] p

2 x **2p** = [   ] p

3 x **2p** = [   ] p

4 x **2p** = [   ] p

5 x **2p** = [   ] p

6 x **2p** = [   ] p

7 x **2p** = [   ] p

8 x **2p** = [   ] p

9 x **2p** = [   ] p

10 x **2p** = [   ] p

Count the legs on each bird and write the number in the box.

2									

4 x 2 =

1 x 2 = ◯

2 x 2 = ◯

3 x 2 = ◯

4 x 2 = ◯

5 x 2 = ◯

6 x 2 = ◯

7 x 2 = ◯

8 x 2 = ◯

9 x 2 = ◯

10 x 2 = ◯

2 x 2 =

7 x 2 =

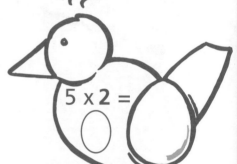

5 x 2 =

10 x 2 =

8 x 2 =

Find the multiples of 2.

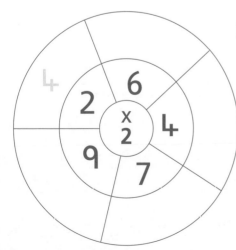

4 x 2 = ◯

6 x 2 = ◯

9 x 2 = ◯

5 x 2 = ◯

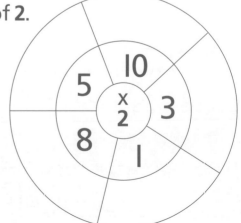

Count **3** across on each line and colour the numbers.

1	2	3	4	5	6	7	8	9	10
11	12	13	14	15	16	17	18	19	20
21	22	23	24	25	26	27	28	29	30

There were **3** in the bed. Colour the **3** family.

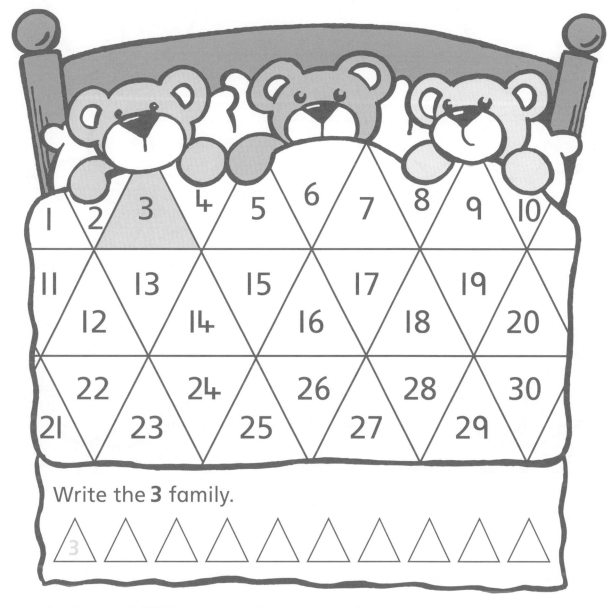

Write the **3** family.

3 △ △ △ △ △ △ △ △ △

Count in **3s** and fill in the missing numbers.

3 ▢ 9 ▢ ▢ 18 ▢ ▢ 27 ▢

3 ⌂ ⌂ 12 ⌂ ⌂ 21 ⌂ ⌂ ⌂

Draw **3** legs on each stool.
Write the number of legs on the stool in the boxes.

| 3 | | = | 3 | legs |

☐ + ☐ = ☐ legs

☐ + ☐ + ☐ = ☐ legs

☐ + ☐ + ☐ + ☐ = ☐ legs

☐ + ☐ + ☐ + ☐ + ☐ = ☐ legs

☐ + ☐ + ☐ + ☐ + ☐ + ☐ = ☐ legs

3 times table

⬭ ⬭ ⬭ ⬭ ⬭ ⬭ ⬭

☐ + ☐ + ☐ + ☐ + ☐ + ☐ + ☐

= ☐ legs

⬭ ⬭ ⬭ ⬭ ⬭ ⬭

☐ + ☐ + ☐ + ☐ + ☐ + ☐

⬭

+ ☐ + ☐ = ☐ legs

⬭ ⬭ ⬭ ⬭ ⬭

☐ + ☐ + ☐ + ☐ + ☐ + ☐

⬭ ⬭ ⬭

+ ☐ + ☐ + ☐ = ☐ legs

⬭ ⬭ ⬭ ⬭ ⬭ ⬭

☐ + ☐ + ☐ + ☐ + ☐ + ☐

⬭ ⬭ ⬭

+ ☐ + ☐ + ☐ + ☐ = ☐ legs

Draw **3** lollipops in each bag.

1 bag has ☐3 lollipops.

2 bags have ☐ lollipops.

3 bags have ☐ lollipops.

4 bags have ☐ lollipops.

5 bags have ☐ lollipops.

6 bags have ☐ lollipops.

7 bags have ☐ lollipops.

8 bags have ☐ lollipops.

9 bags have ☐ lollipops.

10 bags have ☐ lollipops.

5 lots of **3** = ☐   9 lots of **3** = ☐   6 lots of **3** = ☐

7 lots of **3** = ☐   4 lots of **3** = ☐   8 lots of **3** = ☐

2 lots of **3** = ☐   10 lots of **3** = ☐   3 lots of **3** = ☐

How many sheep?

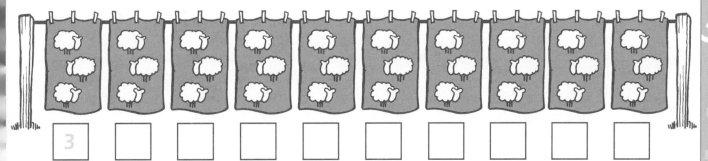

| 3 | | | | | | | | | |

$4 \times \mathbf{3} = \square$ $2 \times \mathbf{3} = \square$ $10 \times \mathbf{3} = \square$

$7 \times \mathbf{3} = \square$ $5 \times \mathbf{3} = \square$ $6 \times \mathbf{3} = \square$

$9 \times \mathbf{3} = \square$ $3 \times \mathbf{3} = \square$ $8 \times \mathbf{3} = \square$

Count in **3**s and fill in the missing numbers.

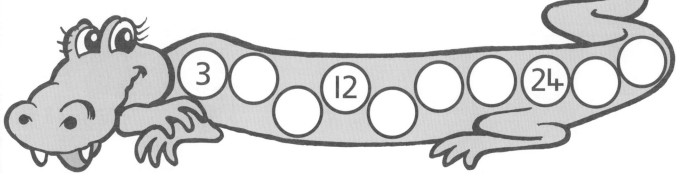

Join the dots.
Count in **3**s.

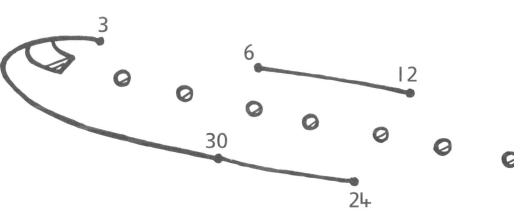

3

6   12   9

30   24   18

27   15   21

Count the spots on each umbrella and write the number in the box.

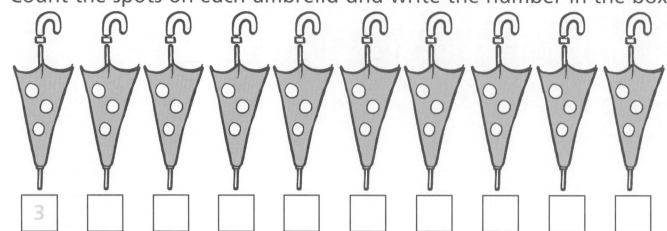

| 3 | | | | | | | | | |

$1 \times 3 = \triangle$

$2 \times 3 = \triangle$

$3 \times 3 = \triangle$

$4 \times 3 = \triangle$

$5 \times 3 = \triangle$

$6 \times 3 = \triangle$

$7 \times 3 = \triangle$

$8 \times 3 = \triangle$

$9 \times 3 = \triangle$

$10 \times 3 = \triangle$

$4 \times 3 = \square$

$7 \times 3 = \square$

$9 \times 3 = \square$

$6 \times 3 = \square$

$10 \times 3 = \square$

$8 \times 3 = \square$

Find the multiples.

$6 \times 3 = \triangledown$

$9 \times 3 = \triangledown$

$7 \times 3 = \triangledown$

$5 \times 3 = \triangledown$

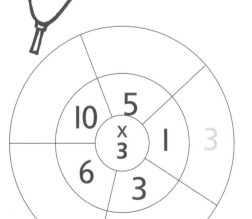

10 5
x
3
1
6
3

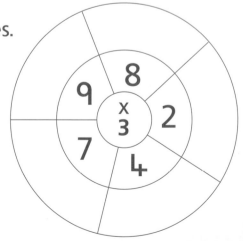

9 8
x
3
2
7
4

Multiply by 2, 3, 5, 10

Multiply by 2

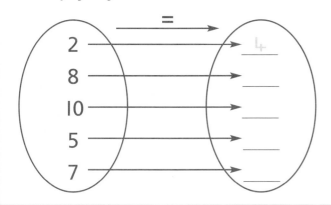

Multiply by 3

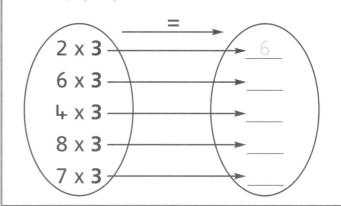

5 times

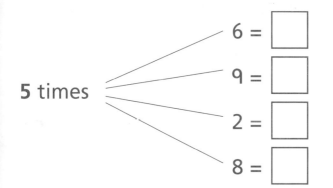

6 = ☐

9 = ☐

2 = ☐

8 = ☐

10 times 8 = ☐

10 times 3 = ☐

10 times 10 = ☐

10 times 6 = ☐

Multiply by 3

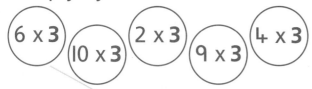

Multiply by 5

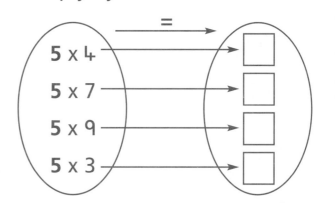

Multiply by 2

6 x **2** = ☐

4 x **2** = ☐

10 x **2** = ☐

8 x **2** = ☐

3 x **2** = ☐

Multiply by 10

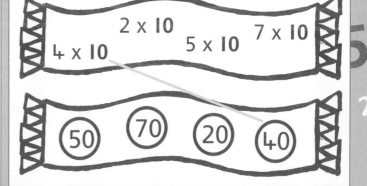

27

Picture problems

How much money has Mark saved?

[ ] x **10**p = [ ] p

Mark has saved [ ] p

Dad stacks his logs in piles of 10. How many logs are there altogether?

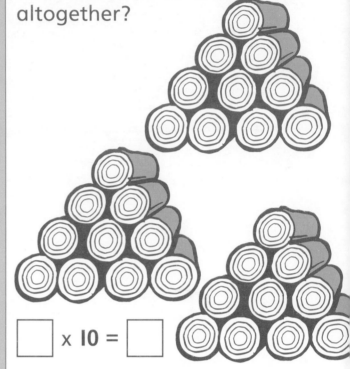

[ ] x **10** = [ ]

Dad has [ ] logs.

The balloon seller has 10 balloons in each bunch. How many balloons does he have?

[ ] x **10** = [ ]

He has [ ] balloons.

There are 10 apples on each tree. How many apples are there?

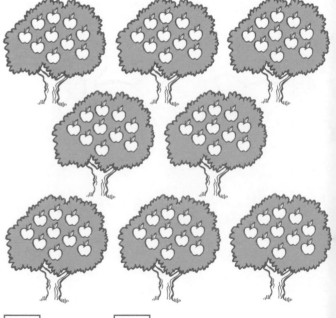

[ ] x **10** = [ ]

There are [ ] apples.

28

Picture problems

Join the dots.
Count in 5s

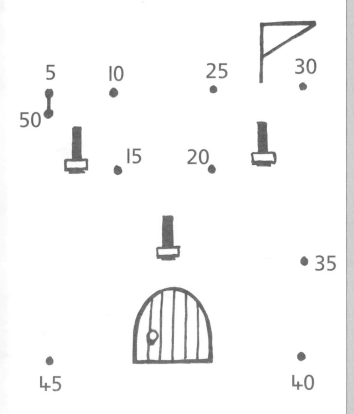

5   10   25   30

50

15   20

35

45   40

How much did Gupta pay for 6 buns?

5p

☐ x 5p = ☐ p

Gupta paid ☐ p

Farmer Scott's hens lay 5 eggs each. He has 4 hens.
How many eggs does he have?

◯ x 5 = ◯

Farmer Scott has ◯ eggs.

On the camp site there are 5 people in each tent.
How many people are there?

△ x 5 = △

There are △ people on the camp site.

29

Picture problems

Jane rolled 3 dice and scored **2** on each. What did she score?

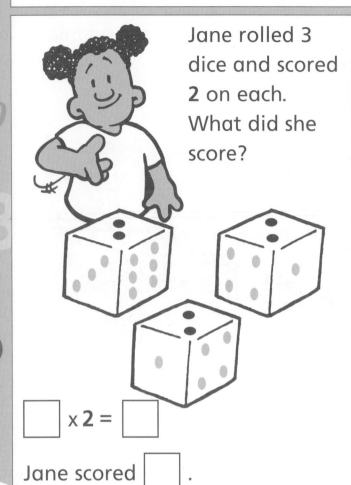

☐ x **2** = ☐

Jane scored ☐ .

Mum bought **5** pairs of shoes. How many shoes did she buy?

☐ x **2** = ☐

She bought ☐ shoes.

Each kite has **2** bows. How many bows are there?

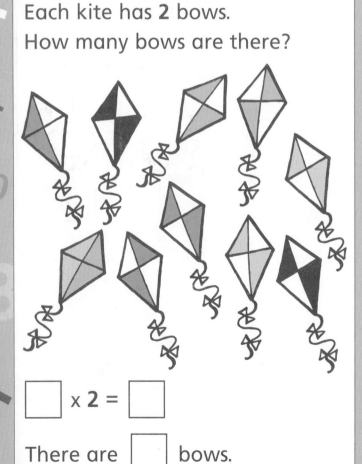

☐ x **2** = ☐

There are ☐ bows.

10 children each catch **2** fish. How many do they catch in total?

☐ x **2** = ☐

They catch ☐ fish.

Picture problems

Zera puts **3** flags in each
sandcastle.
How many flags does she use?

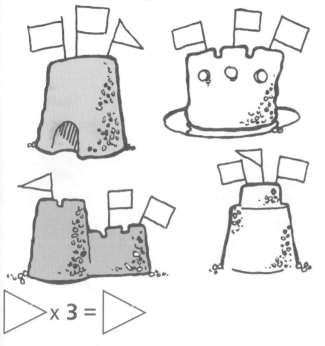

▷ x **3** = ▷

She uses ▷ flags.

Each photograph has **3** people
on it.
How many people are there?

◯ x **3** = ◯

There are ◯ people.

There are **3** apples left on
each tree. How many apples
are there?

◯ x **3** = ◯

There are ◯ apples left.

There are **3** bees buzzing around
each flower. How many bees are
buzzing around?

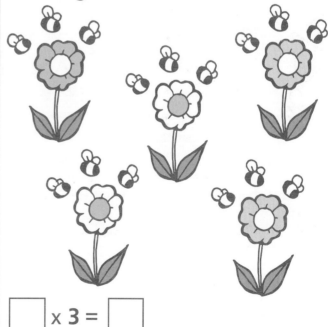

☐ x **3** = ☐

There are ☐ bees.

31

Schofield & Sims
HELPING CHILDREN TO LEARN

Schofield and Sims have, for over a hundred years, published a wide variety of educational materials for use in schools or at home. Specialising in products for Early Years, Key Stage 1 and Key Stage 2, our texts are written by experienced teachers and concentrate on the key areas of Maths, English and Science. The range includes workbooks, revision guides, practice papers, dictionaries and laminated posters.

Times Tables Practice Book 1

Clearly structured exercises to build understanding of and confidence in the times tables. This first book introduces the times tables in an order that reflects Numeracy lessons in schools at Key Stage 1. Includes: x10, x5, x2 and x3.

The second book in the series **Times Tables Practice Book 2** (isbn 0 7217 0960 5) covers the remaining 4, 6, 7, 8, and 9 times tables, as taught at Key Stage 2, with additional word and picture problems applying the use of the times tables in real life situations.

Some of our other Key Stage 1 Maths materials include:

Workbooks

Number Vocabulary – a 4 book series which helps children understand the basic vocabulary necessary
for developing early mathematical skills

NEW Problem Solving – a 3 book series including exercises in using and applying mathematics at Key Stage 1

Key Maths – a 5 book series for children working at levels 1-3 of Key Stage 1

NEW Mental MAths – a 2 book series that helps children to build confidence in their mathematical knowledge and mental agility.

NEW Revision Guide and Practice Papers for Key Stage 1

Maths Posters
• Times Tables   • Number Lines   • Multiplication Squares   • Numbers   • Shapes

Available in most bookshops and many libraries or contact us for more information and a free catalogue:

• Telephone us on 01484 607080

• By sending us a fax on 01484 606815

• E-mail us on sales@schofieldandsims.co.uk

• Direct from our Website www.schofieldandsims.co.uk

Our customer service team will be happy to help with your enquiry

Schofield & Sims
HELPING CHILDREN TO LEARN
Dogley Mill, Fenay Bridge, Huddersfield HD8 0NQ
Phone 01484 607080 Facsimile 01484 606815

ISBN 0-7217-0959-1

9 780721 709598

£1.95
Key Stage 1
Age range 5-7 years